THE
REFLECTIVE JOURNAL
FOR COACHES

SHARPENING YOUR COACHING SKILLS
FOR CLIENT

D1091720

The
Reflective Journal
For Coaches

Sharpening Your Coaching Skills
For Client Results

Keith E. Webb

Active Results LLC

The Reflective Journal For Coaches: Sharpening Your Coaching Skills For Client Results

Active Results LLC
activeresults.com

ISBN 978-1-944000-05-9

Second Edition: October 2021

Table of Contents

Introduction

Coaching is more an art than it is a set of communication skills. Coaching begins not with questions, but rather two people in dialogue on a journey of discovery. It's a journey for both people. The coach discovers right alongside the client.

The more self-aware and reflective the coach is, the more likely she or he will be able to facilitate a process of self-awareness within the other person. Self-awareness keeps our "stuff"—things like our biases, emotions, and need to convince—in check so we remain open, curious, flexible, and client-centered.

The purpose of *The Reflective Journal for Coaches* is for you as a coach to reflect on your coaching and coach training experiences.

Through journaling you can increase your own self-awareness, spot areas for your own personal development, and increase your own learning—all in order to deliver better coaching results for your clients.

Keep coaching!

Dr. Keith E. Webb, PCC

Why Practice Reflection?

Reflection is the ability to think back and observe ourselves in action in order to learn from the experience.

Every day we have experiences that are in some big or small way different than those we have previously encountered. We were not just spectators to those experiences. We thought, felt, and acted (or didn't act) during them.

Often, we are not fully cognitive of what happened, so we miss out on the benefits those experiences might otherwise provide. We fail to learn from them and thus miss opportunities to grow.

Our reflection can produce models of thought and behavior that we want to continue following and also provide warnings of what to avoid in the future.

"We had the experience, but missed the meaning."

—T.S. Eliot

Reflection then, is stopping to consider our experiences and how we thought, felt, and acted during them.

Let me share a personal story of reflecting on my coaching and how it benefitted me, and my clients.

I coach many different types of people. One day, after coaching a particular client I became aware that I had a lot of energy, both mental and physical. My experience with other clients, however, left me feeling blah and lethargic. I had never noticed this before, but this must have been happening for some time.

I spent time reflecting on what I felt during and after a coaching conversation with an "energy draining" experience with a client. During that coaching conversation I had difficulty staying present. The pace was slower than I preferred, and the topic was not personally interesting to me. I felt some boredom. Yet, at the same time I heard a voice in my head saying, "You're a coach. Get over yourself! If you do a good job coaching this person, they will make progress."

Like a good coach, I ended this reflection by creating plans for the next time this situation arose so that I would maintain greater presence and value the conversation for the client's sake.

The next few "energy draining" conversations went better. I also reflected on those conversations. At this point, I noticed a pattern with the coaching topics. I realized that I might not be the right coach for that sort of topic. This suspicion was reinforced as I reflected more deeply on an "energy giving" conversation with a client. We discussed topics I was more interested in.

Through this series of reflections on my coaching conversations I learned how to better engage with people who do not match my pacing or interests. And I learned which client coaching topics I find most interesting and thus easier for me to maintain coaching presence. This learning helped me to tailor my coaching practice to those I could most effectively coach.

Reflection on your coaching has a number of benefits. Reflection...

- Helps you to be intentional about your own personal development.
- Provides professional development as you grow in effectiveness as a coach.
- Gives you rich details of coaching conversations to work on with your mentor-coach or coaching supervisor.
- Results in your clients better reaching their intended outcomes.

Why Write Your Reflections?

The short answer to why write your reflection in a journal is: the process of writing clarifies and deepens your thinking.

A few years ago, I had the brilliant idea of recording my speaking engagements to have transcribed for a draft of a new book I was working on. My presentations were well-received. But when I read the transcript, I was shocked. It was nearly unintelligible!

What was clear in my mind, and even clear to my audiences when I said it, wasn't clear at all when written.

I learned that writing forces a level of clarity beyond thinking about or talking about the topic.

I am often perfectly content with my thoughts and feelings but become dissatisfied when trying to express them in writing.

One of the reasons for this is, we think in scattered and incomplete thoughts and feelings. Writing forces us to name and describe our thoughts and feelings in concrete ways. When writing, we use specific words and sentences to take us beyond incomplete thoughts to deeper reflection.

Reflection ponders the question: What does this experience say to me? Reflection helps us get to meaning and then to learning and then to application.

We ask ourselves tougher questions and stick with them longer when we sit and put our reflections on paper, rather than keeping them only in our minds.

- What caused me to feel this way?
- What kept me from doing something different in that moment?
- Who do I want to *be* as I coach this person?

Only thinking, and not writing, too easily lets us off the hook from grappling with tough questions. We have a tendency to cut short our reflection and move on to other thoughts or tasks. In doing so, we can easily miss what we need to learn to improve our coaching and serve our clients better.

Another benefit of journaling your reflection is it provides a written record, marking milestones along the path of your experience and learning. The value here is you can occasionally review your journal to see the bigger picture of your journey as a coach. You may notice patterns over weeks and months of reflection that you didn't notice during a shorter period of time.

A journal, as a history in action, serves as a reminder of your learning. It becomes your personal coaching training manual. You can review it to see how far you've come and find lessons to implement anew.

What Activities To Reflect On

The reflective coach considers more than just client coaching conversations. Life is rich with experiences that help form you personally and professionally. You can learn from all of them.

A coach's professional development would benefit from reflecting on four types of activities:

1. **Your work with clients.** Reflect on your experience, what you learned, and how you will apply that learning to your future coaching conversations. Below there are suggestions for listening to recordings of your coaching conversations and asking clients for feedback.

2. **Feedback about you from clients.** It is a good practice to occasionally ask your clients for feedback about your coaching. Reflect on that input and apply your learning to further improve client results.

3. **Mentor Coaching or Supervision sessions.** As you meet with a Mentor Coach or coaching Supervisor, you can reflect on what you discussed together. (More on these two roles in the next section.) You can also consider the dynamics of your relationship with your

Mentor Coach or Supervisor. Reflect on a specific conversation and apply it to your coaching.

4. **Professional development activities.** These activities could be workshops, additional coaching training, conferences, seminars, etc. What learning did you gain from the activity and how will you apply it to your coaching practice?

One coaching association, the European Mentoring & Coaching Council, requires applicants of their individual coach credential to provide reflective journal examples of each of these four types of activities.

Listen To Yourself Coach

In my coaching training business we do a lot of work with individual coaches who want to grow in their coaching skills. We stumbled upon a method of helping coaches reflect on their coaching conversations that is so fruitful that we now use the process in all our individual work with coaches.

When I give feedback to coaches on their coaching conversation, they sometimes don't remember saying what I mention. Or they remember it differently, recalling their coaching performance as better or worse than it really was.

All this goes away when the coach listens to a recording of their coaching conversation.

Ask your client for permission to record a coaching conversation. Later, listen to the whole recording, take notes as you go.

As you listen, consider the Reflective Questions for Coaches later in this book. Listen beyond the intentions you had when coaching, to hear what you actually said.

After we began doing this process with coaches, they quickly spotted most of the things I previously needed to point out to them. I affirmed their observations on things to improve, added some additional feedback, and pointed out the many ways they coached well.

I'm still amazed at how powerful it is to listen to yourself coach.

Reflection is for you. It will help you develop as a person and to develop professionally as a coach.

Ask for Feedback from Clients

As you coach through multiple-session coaching engagements with clients, it's a good practice to ask your clients for feedback. Don't wait until the end of the engagement to check in with them. A short discussion midway through the engagement can reinforce what the client has learned and accomplished to that point and allow for helpful mid-course adjustments to the coaching relationship.

I often take a few minutes at the beginning of the fourth or fifth coaching session to check in with the client to ask about their coaching experience and how we're working together. This isn't a long discussion. A few minutes will achieve these two purposes.

Here's how I start, "We've been coaching together for the past 2 months. I'd like to take a few minutes and check in with you about your experience so far and how we're working together. Would that be okay?"

Focus the first couple of questions on the client's learning and experience. These questions draw out the value of the coaching engagement and reinforce the client's learning and progress. You might ask questions like these:

What meaningful insights have you had so far from our coaching conversations?

What action steps moved you the furthest ahead?

What new qualities or strengths have you uncovered in yourself?

Then move to a couple of questions to draw out feedback on their experience working with you as a coach.

So far, how are your expectations of coaching being met?

As your coach, what am I doing that is helpful for you?

How could I be a better coach for you?

Of course, follow each of these questions with clarifying questions to explore beyond their initial responses.

Beyond Self-Reflection

Self-reflection is essential for continual growth. When you pair self-reflection with coaching, you produce even better results. In the world of coaching there are two common types of developmental practices for coaches: Mentor Coaching and Coaching Supervision.

Mentor Coaching assists people in their development as coaches. The focus is specifically on improving their coaching skills based on the use of the International Coaching Federation's (ICF) Core Competencies. A qualified Mentor Coach will observe the coach in action (live or by listening to a recording) and provide developmental feedback. An extended period of time is most helpful for developing your coaching skills. The ICF requires 10 hours of Mentor Coaching over a period of at least 3 months with a qualified mentor coach for applicants of their individual coach credentials.

Coaching Supervision is a process to produce ongoing professional development for coaches. The term "supervision" comes from the similar function used by therapists and shouldn't be confused with a management or oversight function.

Coaching Supervision provides coaches with a safe arena (individually or as part of a group) to process their coaching experiences and work through what's happening inside them as they coach. Coaching Supervision results in collaborative learning to develop coaches and improve the coaching experience for their clients.

Engaging with a Mentor Coach and a Coaching Supervisor are essential activities for coaches. Each role provides distinct types of professional development for coaches to continually develop, resulting in better coaching experiences for you and your clients.

Taking time to journal and reflect on the feedback you received or experience you had with your Mentor Coach or Coaching Supervisor is a way to take that learning further. Dig in deeper and create specific action steps for what you'll do next time in a similar situation.

How To Use This Reflective Journal

Pick A Specific Coaching Conversation

Begin by identifying a specific coaching conversation. It's important to not think generally over several coaching conversations, but rather to reflect specifically on one particular conversation. (The process is the same for reflecting on Client Feedback, Mentor Coaching, or another Learning Activity.)

It's a good practice for newer coaches to reflect often on their coaching conversations. As you progress in your coaching you may scale back the frequency depending on the number of client coaching conversations you have. I recommend reflecting and journaling about a coaching experience at least once a week.

The journal pages begin on page 37. Write the name of the client or activity and the date of that experience. Check the box for what type of coaching experience you will reflect on. This will help you find it later if you want to refer back to it.

Name

Amy Chung

Date

Nov 6, 2021

[X] Coaching
Client

[ ] Client
Feedback

[ ] Mentor Coaching
or Supervision

[ ] Learning
Activity

In the next steps, you will journal your thoughts in four areas: 1) on your experience, 2) your learning, 3) your application, and 4) what ICF coaching competencies relate to your reflection.

1. Reflect on Your Experience

Shortly after the conversation or activity take a few minutes and ask yourself some questions. In the next chapter there are 50 reflection questions to help you.

Reflect on your experience during the coaching conversation. Think about what you did, thought, and felt at the time.

The reflective journal is not usually about the client's issue. It's about what happened in you, in your relationship with the client, and the impact those things had on the conversation. You are looking at you, not the client.

What did I experience during the conversation?

What happened inside me during the conversation?

(There are 25 My Experience Questions on page 31.)

Write a summary of your experience in the first person and provide details of what happened with you.

Coaching With Amy (a good example):

> *"Working with this client, my own solutions kept popping up in my mind. My thoughts went to questions that would move the client toward these solutions. These thoughts distracted me and prevented me from fully listening and being present with the client for their sake."*

Notice how the coach is specific and detailed about what happened inside her during the conversation.

She then reflected on how her experience differed from her coaching model and principles—wanting to provide solutions, not fully listening, and not being fully present for the client's sake.

Now, let's compare this reflection with a poor example of reflecting on the coaching experience.

Coaching with Amy (a poor example):

> *"I've got all kinds of ideas I want to share with my clients. I held back. But it was tough."*

This example isn't specific to one conversation. Instead it generalizes over several coaching conversations and loses impact because of it.

A lack of detail and step-by-step description of what happened limits the usefulness of this description of the coach's experience. Lack of detail here can mean lack of depth in reflection and missed opportunities to apply useful lessons later.

Let's look at another situation, this time beginning with a poor example.

Coaching with Mark (a poor example):

> *"My client has to make a decision about his career but doesn't want to take any risks. I asked him about pros and cons of each option he sees, but he didn't seem to make any progress. It was frustrating for me. I need to find a way to help him move forward."*

This example reflection speaks more to helping the client than the coach. Our reflection isn't about how to solve the client's problem. It's about us, our coaching, and perhaps the client-coach relationship.

We reflect on our coaching so that we can first personally develop, then translate those insights into professional development. By becoming more aware of what's happening in us, we can better serve the client.

Coaching with Mark (a good example):

> *"My client has to make a decision about his career but wants to limit his risk. I found myself becoming impatient with him. I wanted him to make the decision and move forward. Some of my questions tried to "push" him forward, probably not for his sake, but for mine."*

This reflection speaks to what the coach did and felt. The coach's reflection on what she did surfaced the relational insight that she may have "pushed" him to a decision for her own sake.

♨ 2. Reflect on Your Learning

Reflect on your experience to find learning. What do you observe in your experience?

Analyze your experience and compare to the models and principles that inform your coaching. Where does your experience match or fall short?

The International Coaching Federation's 8 Core Competencies provide a helpful standard for skills and approaches in professional coaching. Understanding these coaching competencies and relating your learning and practice to them can help you grow as a coach.

Reflect on your coaching experience through the lenses of your coaching model and the 8 ICF Core Competencies to find understanding and learning.

What does this experience say to me?

What can I learn?

How does my experience differ from my coaching models and principles?

(There are 15 My Learn Questions on page 34.)

Let's continue with the two coaching examples from step 1 to find the learning.

Coaching with Amy:

> *"I risked manipulating the client to my solutions, while at the same time, possibly prevented the client's own solutions from surfacing. I need to quiet my inner 'problem-solver.' The coaching conversation is not about me, it's about the client making their own discoveries."*

In this example, the coach recognizes the possible impact of getting caught up in her own solutions for the client, including manipulating the client and preventing the client from reaching his or her own solutions.

This awareness helps the coach to see more clearly two ways she was putting herself at the center of the coaching conversation. She recognized her "inner problem-solver" and her ego jumping in.

Let's look at the second coaching example:

Coaching with Mark:

> *"My impatience shouldn't be the measure of when it's time to move forward. Some of the feelings I experienced may be more about me than the client. I need to allow the client to work at his own pace, not my pace. And not project any of my own needs for achievement onto him."*

The coach identified her impatience and reflected on her feelings to find more learning.

After observing her thoughts and feelings, the coach suspects she may be projecting some of her own psychological needs for achievement and progress onto the client. Whether it is true or not, it is a helpful observation. Just the fact that the coach suspects it may make it a good topic of conversation with a Coaching Supervisor.

These observations and learning now set the coach up to create action plans for the next time she experiences this situation. That's the next step.

✿ 3. Apply to Your Practice

After reflecting on your experience (what you did, thought, and felt) and your learning (your observations, reflection, and synthesis), apply those insights to your practice. Consider what options you have for the next time you face a similar situation.

What specifically do I intend to *do* based on my reflection?

(There are 10 My Application Questions on page 35.)

Let's go back to our examples above and apply our learning to them.

Coaching with Amy:

> *"Next time solutions begin popping into my mind, I will recognize sooner what is happening internally for me. I will make a choice to put aside my ideas and to focus on helping the client to explore their own solutions. Solutions may come to my mind as I coach others, but I will be able to manage them with greater awareness and skill to engage the client."*

This description is specific and concrete enough to be memorable. The application provides a strategy with specific steps to implement the learning in future coaching conversations.

Coaching with Mark:

> *"When I feel myself becoming impatient, I will recognize that feeling and not let it hijack the conversation. I will look again to the client as the guide for pacing, progress, and timing. If it's appropriate, I will use client-oriented language to share any feedback or observations. At all times, I will keep the conversation about the client and not me."*

Several possible strategies emerge from the learning regarding the coach's impatience. These strategies synthesize well with the coach's principles or frameworks for coaching.

ICF   4. Relate to the ICF Core Competencies

A final step is to relate your learning and practice to International Coaching Federation Core Competencies. Doing this step will increase your awareness and understanding of the competencies and further support your growth as a coach.

The complete list of ICF Core Competencies is at the back of this journal.

Which ICF Core Competencies relate to my learning?

Coaching with Amy:

"Maintains Presence and Listens Actively."

Coaching with Mark:

"Maintains Presence and Evokes Awareness."

Now you are ready to begin. On the next few pages are a list of 50 Questions for the Reflective Coach. Pick a conversation and fill in your first journal entry.

Don't forget to occasionally review what you've written in your journal to remind yourself of your previous experiences, lessons, and plans for application.

As you read through your journal look for themes and trends. What can you celebrate? What do you want to reflect on further? Perhaps reading through your journal and reflecting on it could be a journal entry in itself.

50 Questions For The Reflective Coach

My Experience Questions

What I Did

- What did I do well as coach?
- What did I do that didn't seem to further the client's awareness?
- What approaches did I use? What happened? What alternatives might I have tried?
- In what ways did I practice the model or principle I intended to?
- Consider who led each part of the conversation—me or the client?

What I Thought

- What thoughts did I have during the conversation?
- At what point(s) did my mind wonder? Where did it go? What triggered it?
- Where did I feel most engaged in this conversation?

- How much was this conversation about me?
- What was my level of presence during the conversation?

How I Felt

- What emotions did I experience?
- What emotions did I feel for the client?
- When ... happened ... I felt...
- How did I feel about myself during the conversation?
- How was my self-image present in the conversation?

My Mindset

- How would I describe my mindset during this conversation?
- What might have made this conversation more successful?
- What beliefs and values were not fully honored?
- Where did I find my mindset challenged?
- What parts of the conversation engaged my heart? Which parts didn't?

My Relationship With the Client

- How did the client and I relate during the conversation?
- What dynamics did I encounter in my relationship with the client?
- What input did I receive from the client regarding my coaching?
- How did I show up in the conversation? As expert, mother, friend, hero, impartial observer, etc...

- What level of responsibility to perform or deliver results for the client did I feel?

My Learning Questions

My Observations

- I noticed that I …
- What observations do I have about myself in this coaching conversation?
- What am I ignoring or playing down?
- What shifts do I need to make?
- What systemic issues do I see?
- What processes did I encounter?
- What external dynamics (cultural, systems, processes) did I encounter?

My Learning

- What conclusions can I draw from my experience?
- What would I advise myself about my coaching?
- What can I learn from this experience?

My Models and Principles

- How does my experience link to my coaching models and principles?
  What ethical areas did I touch on?
- What additional skill development do I need?
- What models or principles were most relevant to this conversation?
- From my understanding of psychology or personality, what dynamics did I observe in myself or in my relationship with the client?

My Application Questions

My Options

- What options do I see for the next time I encounter this situation?
- What strategy would I like to use next time?
- Based on my learning, what are a couple of options?
- What professional development do I need as a coach?
- What learning assignments do I want to give myself?

My Applications

- What will I do next time a similar situation arises?
- What personal development steps will I commit to?
- What are my next steps toward greater mastery?
- What are my next steps to development personally?
- If I do what I am committing to, what effect do I expect to see in myself or in my relationship with the client?

Journal Pages

Name

Date

☐ Coaching
   Client

☐ Client
   Feedback

☐ Mentor Coaching
   or Supervision

☐ Learning
   Activity

My Experience

My Learning

My Application

Related Core Competencies

ICF

Name

Date

- [ ] Coaching Client
- [ ] Client Feedback
- [ ] Mentor Coaching or Supervision
- [ ] Learning Activity

My Experience

My Learning

....

....

....

....

....

....

....

....

My Application

....

....

....

....

....

....

....

....

....

....

....

....

Related Core Competencies

....

....

....

Name

Date

☐ Coaching ☐ Client ☐ Mentor Coaching ☐ Learning
Client Feedback or Supervision Activity

My Experience

My Learning

My Application

Related Core Competencies

Name

Date

☐ Coaching
Client

☐ Client
Feedback

☐ Mentor Coaching
or Supervision

☐ Learning
Activity

My Experience

My Learning

My Application

Related Core Competencies

Name

Date

☐ Coaching
Client

☐ Client
Feedback

☐ Mentor Coaching
or Supervision

☐ Learning
Activity

My Experience

....

....

....

....

....

....

....

....

....

....

....

....

....

....

My Learning

....

....

....

....

....

....

....

....

....

....

....

My Application

....

....

....

....

....

....

....

....

....

....

....

Related Core Competencies

....

....

....

Name

Date

☐ Coaching
  Client

☐ Client
  Feedback

☐ Mentor Coaching
  or Supervision

☐ Learning
  Activity

My Experience

My Learning

....
....
....
....
....
....
....

My Application

....
....
....
....
....
....
....
....
....
....
....
....
....

Related Core Competencies

....
....
....

Name   Date

☐ Coaching
   Client

☐ Client
   Feedback

☐ Mentor Coaching
   or Supervision

☐ Learning
   Activity

My Experience

My Learning

....

....

....

....

....

....

....

My Application

....

....

....

....

....

....

....

....

....

....

....

Related Core Competencies

....

....

....

Name

Date

☐ Coaching
　 Client

☐ Client
　 Feedback

☐ Mentor Coaching
　 or Supervision

☐ Learning
　 Activity

My Experience

....

....

....

....

....

....

....

....

....

....

....

....

....

....

....

....

My Learning

....

....

....

....

....

....

....

....

....

....

....

....

My Application

....

....

....

....

....

....

....

....

....

....

....

Related Core Competencies

....

....

....

Name

Date

☐ Coaching
 Client

☐ Client
 Feedback

☐ Mentor Coaching
 or Supervision

☐ Learning
 Activity

My Experience

....

....

....

....

....

....

....

....

....

....

....

....

....

....

....

My Learning

....

....

....

....

....

....

....

....

....

....

....

My Application

....

....

....

....

....

....

....

....

....

....

....

Related Core Competencies

....

....

....

Name

Date

☐ Coaching Client   ☐ Client Feedback   ☐ Mentor Coaching or Supervision   ☐ Learning Activity

My Experience

My Learning

....

....

....

....

....

....

....

My Application

....

....

....

....

....

....

....

....

....

....

....

Related Core Competencies

....

....

....

Name

Date

☐ Coaching
　 Client

☐ Client
　 Feedback

☐ Mentor Coaching
　 or Supervision

☐ Learning
　 Activity

My Experience

....
....
....
....
....
....
....
....
....
....
....
....
....
....
....
....

My Learning

....
....
....
....

My Application

Related Core Competencies

Name

Date

☐ Coaching
  Client

☐ Client
  Feedback

☐ Mentor Coaching
  or Supervision

☐ Learning
  Activity

My Experience

....

....

....

....

....

....

....

....

....

....

....

My Learning

....

....

....

....

_____

_____

_____

_____

_____

_____

_____

My Application

_____

_____

_____

_____

_____

_____

_____

_____

_____

_____

_____

Related Core Competencies

_____

_____

_____

Name

Date

☐ Coaching
Client

☐ Client
Feedback

☐ Mentor Coaching
or Supervision

☐ Learning
Activity

My Experience

My Learning

....

....

....

....

....

....

....

My Application

....

....

....

....

....

....

....

....

....

....

....

Related Core Competencies

....

....

....

Name

Date

☐ Coaching
   Client

☐ Client
   Feedback

☐ Mentor Coaching
   or Supervision

☐ Learning
   Activity

My Experience

My Learning

....

....

....

....

....

....

....

My Application

....

....

....

....

....

....

....

....

....

....

....

Related Core Competencies

....

....

....

Name

Date

☐ Coaching
   Client

☐ Client
   Feedback

☐ Mentor Coaching
   or Supervision

☐ Learning
   Activity

My Experience

My Learning

....

....

....

....

....

....

....

My Application

....

....

....

....

....

....

....

....

....

....

....

Related Core Competencies

....

....

....

Name

Date

☐ Coaching
Client

☐ Client
Feedback

☐ Mentor Coaching
or Supervision

☐ Learning
Activity

My Experience

My Learning

My Application

Related Core Competencies

Name

Date

☐ Coaching ☐ Client ☐ Mentor Coaching ☐ Learning
   Client   Feedback   or Supervision   Activity

My Experience

My Learning

....

....

....

....

....

....

....

My Application

....

....

....

....

....

....

....

....

....

....

....

Related Core Competencies

....

....

....

Name

Date

☐ Coaching
Client

☐ Client
Feedback

☐ Mentor Coaching
or Supervision

☐ Learning
Activity

My Experience

My Learning

My Application

Related Core Competencies

Name

Date

☐ Coaching
Client

☐ Client
Feedback

☐ Mentor Coaching
or Supervision

☐ Learning
Activity

My Experience

My Learning

....

....

....

....

....

....

....

....

My Application

....

....

....

....

....

....

....

....

....

....

....

....

Related Core Competencies

....

....

....

Name

Date

☐ Coaching
Client

☐ Client
Feedback

☐ Mentor Coaching
or Supervision

☐ Learning
Activity

My Experience

My Learning

....

....

....

....

....

....

....

My Application

....

....

....

....

....

....

....

....

....

....

....

Related Core Competencies

....

....

....

Appendix: ICF Core Competencies

The following eight Core Competencies were developed to support greater understanding about the skills and approaches used within today's coaching profession as defined by the ICF.

The Core Competencies will also support you in calibrating your level of alignment between the coach specific training expected and the training you have experienced. Finally, these competencies are used as the foundation for the ICF coach credentialing examination.

The core competencies are grouped into four clusters that fit together logically. The groupings and individual competencies are not weighted – they do not represent any kind of priority; in that they are all core or critical for any competent coach to demonstrate.

A. Foundation

1. Demonstrates Ethical Practice

Definition: Understands and consistently applies coaching ethics and standards of coaching

1. Demonstrates personal integrity and honesty in interactions with clients, sponsors and relevant stakeholders
2. Is sensitive to clients' identity, environment, experiences, values and beliefs
3. Uses language appropriate and respectful to clients, sponsors and relevant stakeholders
4. Abides by the ICF Code of Ethics and upholds the Core Values
5. Maintains confidentiality with client information per stakeholder agreements and pertinent laws
6. Maintains the distinctions between coaching, consulting, psychotherapy and other support professions
7. Refers clients to other support professionals, as appropriate

2. Embodies a Coaching Mindset
Definition: Develops and maintains a mindset that is open, curious, flexible and client-centered

1. Acknowledges that clients are responsible for their own choices
2. Engages in ongoing learning and development as a coach
3. Develops an ongoing reflective practice to enhance one's coaching
4. Remains aware of and open to the influence of context and culture on self and others
5. Uses awareness of self and one's intuition to benefit clients

6. Develops and maintains the ability to regulate one's emotions
7. Mentally and emotionally prepares for sessions
8. Seeks help from outside sources when necessary

B. Co-Creating the Relationship

3. Establishes and Maintains Agreements
Definition: Partners with the client and relevant stakeholders to create clear agreements about the coaching relationship, process, plans and goals. Establishes agreements for the overall coaching engagement as well as those for each coaching session.

1. Explains what coaching is and is not and describes the process to the client and relevant stakeholders
2. Reaches agreement about what is and is not appropriate in the relationship, what is and is not being offered, and the responsibilities of the client and relevant stakeholders
3. Reaches agreement about the guidelines and specific parameters of the coaching relationship such as logistics, fees, scheduling, duration, termination, confidentiality and inclusion of others
4. Partners with the client and relevant stakeholders to establish an overall coaching plan and goals
5. Partners with the client to determine client-coach compatibility

6. Partners with the client to identify or reconfirm what they want to accomplish in the session
7. Partners with the client to define what the client believes they need to address or resolve to achieve what they want to accomplish in the session
8. Partners with the client to define or reconfirm measures of success for what the client wants to accomplish in the coaching engagement or individual session
9. Partners with the client to manage the time and focus of the session
10. Continues coaching in the direction of the client's desired outcome unless the client indicates otherwise
11. Partners with the client to end the coaching relationship in a way that honors the experience

4. Cultivates Trust and Safety

Definition: Partners with the client to create a safe, supportive environment that allows the client to share freely. Maintains a relationship of mutual respect and trust.

1. Seeks to understand the client within their context which may include their identity, environment, experiences, values and beliefs
2. Demonstrates respect for the client's identity, perceptions, style and language and adapts one's coaching to the client
3. Acknowledges and respects the client's unique talents, insights and work in the coaching process

4. Shows support, empathy and concern for the client
5. Acknowledges and supports the client's expression of feelings, perceptions, concerns, beliefs and suggestions
6. Demonstrates openness and transparency as a way to display vulnerability and build trust with the client

5. Maintains Presence
Definition: Is fully conscious and present with the client, employing a style that is open, flexible, grounded and confident

1. Remains focused, observant, empathetic and responsive to the client
2. Demonstrates curiosity during the coaching process
3. Manages one's emotions to stay present with the client
4. Demonstrates confidence in working with strong client emotions during the coaching process
5. Is comfortable working in a space of not knowing
6. Creates or allows space for silence, pause or reflection

C. Communicating Effectively

6. Listens Actively
Definition: Focuses on what the client is and is not saying to fully understand what is being

communicated in the context of the client systems and to support client self-expression

1. Considers the client's context, identity, environment, experiences, values and beliefs to enhance understanding of what the client is communicating
2. Reflects or summarizes what the client communicated to ensure clarity and understanding
3. Recognizes and inquires when there is more to what the client is communicating
4. Notices, acknowledges and explores the client's emotions, energy shifts, non-verbal cues or other behaviors
5. Integrates the client's words, tone of voice and body language to determine the full meaning of what is being communicated
6. Notices trends in the client's behaviors and emotions across sessions to discern themes and patterns

7. Evokes Awareness

Definition: Facilitates client insight and learning by using tools and techniques such as powerful questioning, silence, metaphor or analogy

1. Considers client experience when deciding what might be most useful
2. Challenges the client as a way to evoke awareness or insight
3. Asks questions about the client, such as their way of thinking, values, needs, wants and beliefs

4. Asks questions that help the client explore beyond current thinking
5. Invites the client to share more about their experience in the moment
6. Notices what is working to enhance client progress
7. Adjusts the coaching approach in response to the client's needs
8. Helps the client identify factors that influence current and future patterns of behavior, thinking or emotion
9. Invites the client to generate ideas about how they can move forward and what they are willing or able to do
10. Supports the client in reframing perspectives
11. Shares observations, insights and feelings, without attachment, that have the potential to create new learning for the client

D. Cultivating Learning and Growth

8. Facilitates Client Growth
Definition: Partners with the client to transform learning and insight into action. Promotes client autonomy in the coaching process.

1. Works with the client to integrate new awareness, insight or learning into their worldview and behaviors
2. Partners with the client to design goals, actions and accountability measures that integrate and expand new learning

3. Acknowledges and supports client autonomy in the design of goals, actions and methods of accountability
4. Supports the client in identifying potential results or learning from identified action steps
5. Invites the client to consider how to move forward, including resources, support and potential barriers
6. Partners with the client to summarize learning and insight within or between sessions
7. Celebrates the client's progress and successes
8. Partners with the client to close the session

https://coachfederation.org/core-competencies

About The Author

Dr. Keith E. Webb is a Professional Certified Coach, author, and speaker specializing in leadership development. He founded and leads a global training company focused on enabling organizations to simultaneously develop the capacity of people, while achieving organizational results. For 20 years, Keith lived in Japan, Indonesia, and Singapore where he designed and delivered leadership development programs. Keith created The COACH Model® and the ICF-approved Professional Coach Certificate Program and has trained leaders in more than 30 countries. He is past President of the ICF Washington State Chapter and the author of seven books. Keith lives near Seattle and blogs at keithwebb.com.